Spelling Practice

Scholastic Children's Books
Euston House,
24 Eversholt Street,
London NW1 1DB, UK

A division of Scholastic Ltd
London • New York • Toronto • Sydney • Auckland
Mexico City • New Delhi • Hong Kong

Book packaging by Blooberry Design

Published in the UK by Scholastic Ltd, 2017

ISBN 978 1407 16617 9

Printed in Malaysia

2 4 6 8 10 9 7 5 3 1

www.scholastic.co.uk

Welcome to the Disney Learning Programme!

Children learn best when they are having fun!

The **Disney Learning Workbooks** are an engaging way for your child to develop their English skills along with fun characters from the wonderful world of Disney.

The **Disney Learning Workbooks** are carefully levelled to present new challenges to developing learners. This workbook has been designed to support the National Curriculum for English at Key Stage 1. It includes activities that practise skills learned at school, which can be consolidated in a relaxed home setting with parental support. Stickers and a range of spelling, writing and craft activities related to *Frozen Magic of the Northern Lights* ensure that children have fun while learning.

Spelling requires children to apply their phonic knowledge when they write words down. By the end of Key Stage 1, children are expected to be able to correctly spell many words, some of which do not follow common spelling patterns. This takes time to master – practice is important, so that spelling becomes effortless. There are some useful tips on pages 42–43. Accurate spelling is a crucial part of the writing process and being a confident speller ensures children can communicate all their wonderful ideas and stories.

This book includes 'Take a Break' sections, which are fun activities related to *Frozen Magic of the Northern Lights*. Keep spelling sessions short and fun. Your child may wish to work independently on some activities or you may enjoy doing them together – either way is fine.

Have fun with the **Disney Learning** programme!

Developed in conjunction with Charlotte Raby, educational consultant

Let's Practise Reading and Writing

In this book, you will find lots of activities to help you practise spelling. You will find these tricky words.

said	says	are	were
was	is	his	has
you	your	be	he
me	she	we	no
go	so	by	my
here	there	where	love
come	some	one	friend

Learning new things can be hard, so don't worry if you find spelling new words tricky. The more you practise, the easier it will get.

Tips to Help

When you want to spell a word:

※ Say the word out loud.

※ Listen carefully to each sound in the word.

※ Think carefully about which letters make each sound.

※ Write the letters down in order.

※ You can check your answers on pages 45–46.

Ask a grown-up to help you to read the instructions if you are not sure what to do.

Let's Write Words

Read the alphabet out loud slowly. Sound out each letter.

a b c d e f g h i j k l m
n o p q r s t u v w x y z

Look at these characters and the words next to them.
The first letters (graphemes) are missing.

Say each name out loud and write in the missing letter.
Now add a sticker of each character.

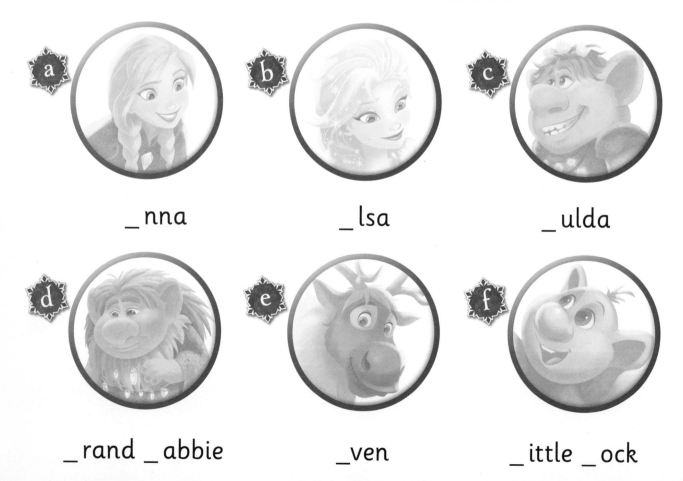

a   _ nna

b   _ lsa

c   _ ulda

d   _ rand _ abbie

e   _ ven

f   _ ittle _ ock

Remember, vowels are a, e, i, o and u.

Now look at these characters. Fill in the missing vowels, then say each name out loud. Can you find the matching stickers of these friends?

g   Sv_n

h   Kr_st_ff

i   _l_f

This time, circle the vowels in these words.

 j   Oaken

 k   Arendelle

 l   The Northern Lights

Let's Learn the Long a Sound

These words all have the long a sound. Read each word out loud, then look at how the long a sound is written. Write the words in the correct boxes.

| paint | day | tail | frame | wait |
| stay | shake | cage | sail | late |

ay

ai

a_e

If the spelling is a_e, you will also need a consonant, for example, take.

Now draw pictures of these three long a words.
Which long a spelling do they use? Tick the box each time.

rain

ay ☐

ai ☐

a_e ☐

play

ay ☐

ai ☐

a_e ☐

cake

ay ☐

ai ☐

a_e ☐

Let's Spell the Days of the Week

The days of the week all end in the **ay** spelling of the **long a** sound. Read the days of the week out loud, then add the word stickers in order.

> **Monday   Tuesday   Wednesday   Thursday**
> **Friday   Saturday   Sunday**

a Anna played outdoors on ⬚ .

b Bulda gave Sven a treat on ⬚ .

c Oaken worked hard on ⬚ .

d Little Rock found two crystals on ⬚ .

e Elsa made magic on ⬚ .

f Olaf and the Snowgies had fun on ⬚ .

g Kristoff went for a walk on ⬚ .

These words all end in the letter y, but they don't all sound the same. Read the words and listen to the sound the y makes. Can you sort the words into the right boxes?

happy   cry   dry   baby   family

fly   funny   sty   party   try

ee sound

igh sound

Now trace over the letters to finish these words.

Sven's reindeer fur is

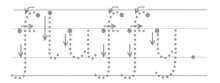

Olaf looks

Take a Break

Follow the letters around the snowflake in alphabetical order. Use a pencil to join the letters. You can use the alphabet line to help you.

Try to complete the puzzle without taking your pencil off the paper!

a b c d e f g h i j k l m

Let's try spelling the names of these characters.
Look at the pictures, then fill in the crossword.

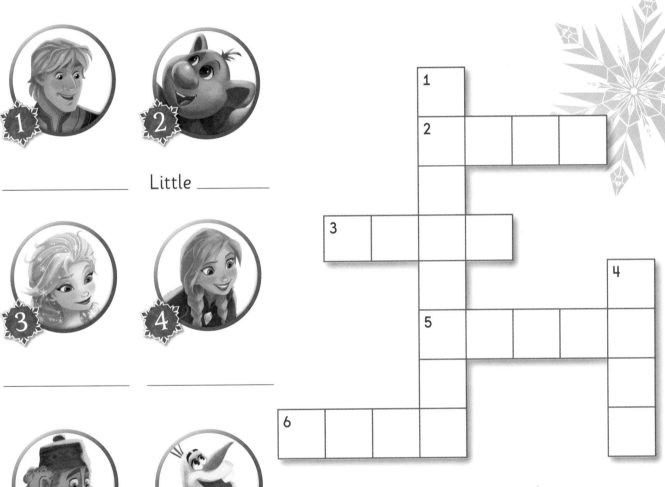

Little _____

n o p q r s t u v w x y z

Let's Spell Words with Double Letters

When a word has a short vowel sound – a, e, i, o or u –
followed by the sounds z, s, l or f, you double these letters.
These letters keep the short vowel sound safe.

Circle the vowel sound in these words.

a well   **b** buzz   **c** miss   **d** off

What sound does each vowel make? Say the sounds out loud.

Draw lines to the correct double letter words and finish these
sentences. Now circle all the double letters in the activity.

e Elsa wears a beautiful blue

f Anna hiked up a snowy

g Olaf gives the flower a

h Sven the reindeer has a coat of

hill.

dress.

fuzz.

sniff.

These double letters have disappeared from the words below.
Write them in the spaces to finish the words.

nn   ll   ff   ll

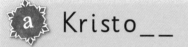 **a** Kristo__

 **c** A__a

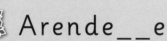 **b** Arende__e

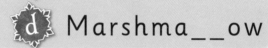 **d** Marshma__ow

Colour in the pictures using the coloured dots to help you.

Let's Join Words

A **compound word** is **made** up of two words joined together. **Each part is spelled the same as if it were on its own.**

'Snowball' is a compound word.

snow + ball = snowball

Draw lines to make five compound words.

a	out	man
b	moon	light
c	snow	doors
d	friend	fall
e	water	ship

Page 6

Page 10

Friday

Tuesday

Saturday

Wednesday

Monday

Sunday

Thursday

Page 7

Page 32

un   un

un   un

un   un

Page 35

huge   moon

cool   due

blew   tune

Pages 40 to 41

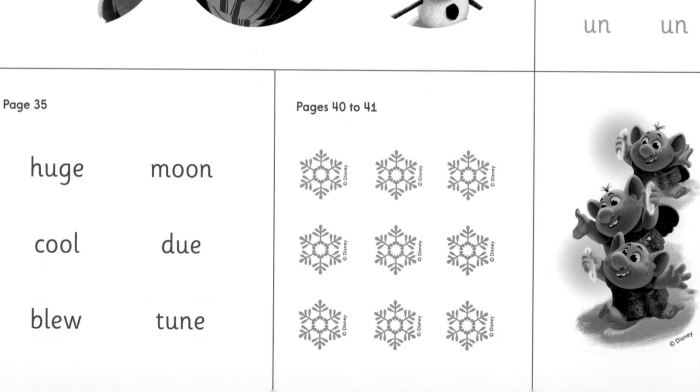

Let's Spell Tricky Words

These words have a tricky bit, which makes them harder to spell. Say the letter sounds you know out loud, then circle the tricky bit using a pen or pencil.

be

he

there

me

where

we

here

she

Let's Spell Words with Long Vowel Sounds

Read the words. Look at how the long o sound is written.
Sort the words into the correct boxes.

snow toast stone foe blow road

boat glow alone yellow roast toe

ow	oe	o_e	oa

If the spelling is o_e, you will also need a consonant, for example, rope.

Draw a circle around the words that have a long o sound and a rectangle around the words that have a short o sound.

hope

code

not

rock

cod

note

rod

hop

rode

Take a Break

Can you think of a Frozen-themed word for each letter of the alphabet? Write the words below. If you can't think of a word that starts with the letter, choose a word that ends in the letter.

a   Arendelle

b

c

d

e

f

g

h

i

j

k

l

m _____

n _____

o _____

p _____

q _____

r _____

s _____

t _____

u _____

v _____

w _____

x _____

y _____

z _____

Let's Learn About Syllables

A syllable is like a 'beat' in a spoken word.

Here's an easy way to find out how many syllables there are in a word.

* Put your hand under your chin.
* Say the word.
* How many times does your chin touch your hand?

This is the number of syllables!

Try clapping to find syllables, too. 1 clap = 1 syllable.

a Say these words out loud. Draw a line in the word where the first syllable ends. The first one has been done for you.

O|laf   crystal   snowflake

mountain   princess   river

water   sisters

Let's Learn About Syllables

Can you find the missing syllables for the words in the snowflakes? Write the letters, then say each word out loud.

deer

i

snow

day

ant

toff

yel

side

a) rein _ _ _ _

b) _ _ _ _ ball

c) _ _ _ ler

d) birth _ _ _

e) _ _ _ low

f) out _ _ _ _

g) Kris _ _ _ _

h) hol _day

Let's Spell Words Ending in ch or tch

Remember, vowels are a, e, i, o and u.

Say these words out loud, then circle the vowel sounds.

a

hatch   bench   ditch

patch   church   beach   watch

stretch   itch   touch

b   Now sort the words by their ch and tch endings.

ch	tch

Trace over the letters to finish the word.

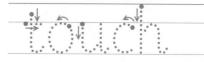

24

Let's spell some more tricky words.
Say the letter sounds you know, then circle the
tricky bit using a pen or pencil.

w(a s)

Now say the word again, but this time say it in a silly way
– say the word as it is spelled!

a Circle the tricky bit in each word below. Then say each
word in a silly way to help you remember how it is spelled.

said	are
was	come
says	were
love	some

Let's Learn Suffixes

A suffix is a word ending, such as ed or ing. You can add suffixes to some words to make new words.

Read the words on the left, then write the words in the crystals, adding ed to the end of each.

+ ed

walk _____

pull _____

lift _____

open _____

lick _____

rush _____

climb _____

jump _____

This time, write the words in the crystals adding ing to the end of each word. What new words will you make?

+ ing

carry _____

work _____

sing _____

sleep _____

play _____

hold _____

watch _____

kick _____

Let's Learn Plurals

Plural means 'more than one'. We can make words plural by adding s at the end. Try turning these words into plurals. Copy the words into the crystals, then add s at the end.

+ s

sister

bird

throne

boat

horse

block

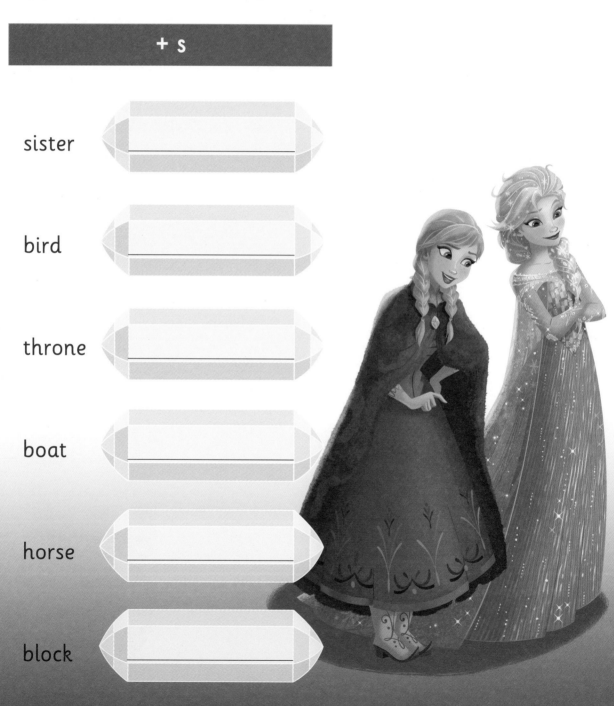

Words that end in sh, ch, tch, x, ss and zz need to have es added to them to make them plural. Turn these words into plurals by adding es each time.

+ es

dish _____

branch _____

catch _____

box _____

dress _____

buzz _____

Join the letters in alphabetical order to reveal who is chasing snowflakes. Use a pencil to join the letters. You can use the alphabet line to help you.

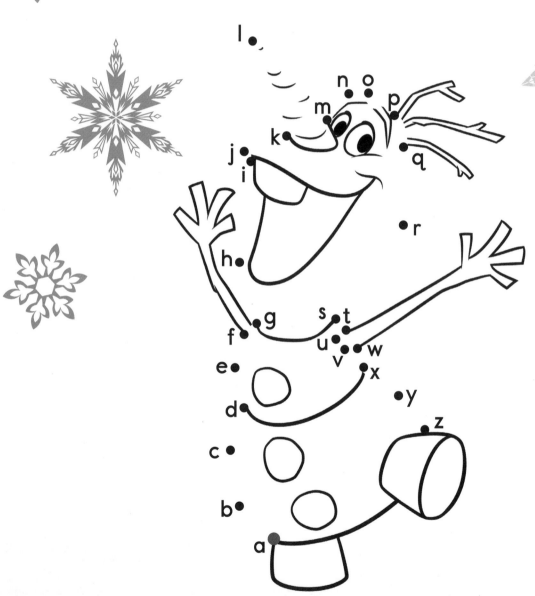

a b c d e f g h i j k l m n o p q r s t u v w x y z

Kristoff is good friends with Olaf and Sven,
he could spot them from miles away.
Can you do it, too? Tick the box of
the correct shadow.

Sven

Olaf

Let's Add the Prefix un-

When we add a prefix to the beginning of a word, it changes the word's meaning. Add stickers with the prefix un in the space below each time.

a   Anna used to think her sister was [ ] kind.

b   Olaf is never [ ] happy!

c   Skating on the ice is [ ] safe for reindeer.

d   Anna used a key to [ ] lock the castle door.

e   Elsa was feeling [ ] adventurous that day.

f   Marshmallow is an [ ] friendly snowman.

Can you see that the words now have a different meaning?

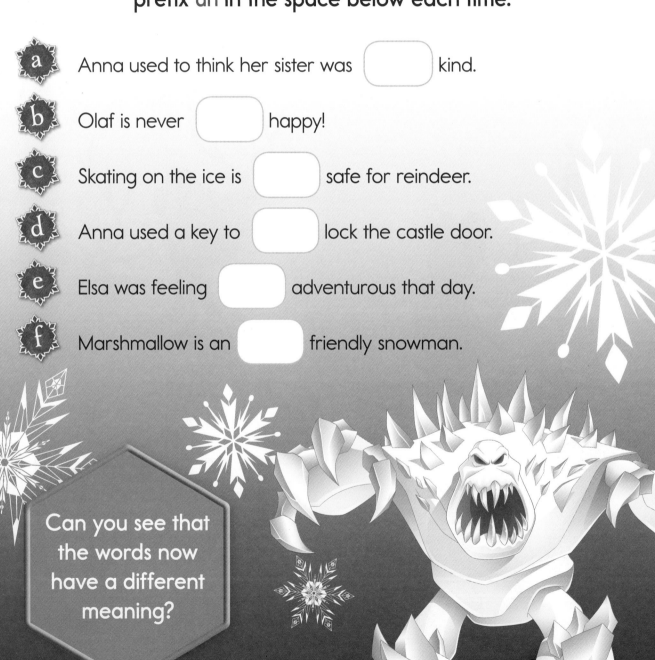

These new words all have a tricky bit, which makes
them harder to spell. Write out the words again, using
a different colour to make the tricky bit stand out.

is   _____   his   _____   has   _____

you   _____   your   _____   no   _____

go   _____   so   _____   by   _____

my   _____   I   _____

Sometimes a picture and words can
help you remember tricky spellings.
Read the rhyme out loud, then
colour in the friends!

i to the end
will be your
friend

Let's Spell Words with Long Vowels

Read the words out loud and listen for the oo sound. Circle the letters that make the oo sound each time.

grew   clue   food

few   soon   blue

true   rule   rescue

rude   new   balloon

If the spelling is u_e, you will also need a consonant, for example, cute.

Now can you sort the words into the correct boxes?

oo	ue	ew	u_e

This time, choose which oo word sticker
will finish these sentences.

| huge | moon | blew |
| cool | due | tune |

a) Little Rock whistled a happy _____ .

b) Elsa was _____ home any minute.

c) Kristoff noticed it was a full _____ .

d) The icy wind _____ a chill through Arendelle.

e) Olaf always stays _____ !

f) Marshmallow looks _____ next to the Snowgies.

Let's Add Suffixes
-er and -est

Choose a word with an **er** suffix from the list to finish these sentences. Cross out the words you don't need.

 a   Elsa needed a   grander / quieter / faster   sled to reach the castle in time.

 b   Anna wore a   thicker / older / smaller   cape to keep her warm.

 c   The Northern Lights were   darker / brighter / slower   than Little Rock could ever have imagined.

Let's Add Suffixes -er and -est

Choose the word with the right suffix **er** or **est**, so that these sentences make sense. Cross out the word you don't need each time.

a   Anna is   bigger / biggest   than Olaf, but Marshmallow is the   bigger / biggest .

b   Elsa was   quicker / quickest   to climb the tree than Kristoff, but Anna was   quicker / quickest .

c   Monday was   cold / colder   than Tuesday, but Friday was the   colder / coldest .

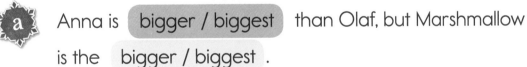

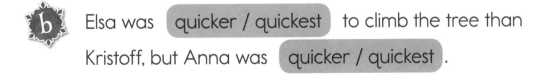

Let's Make It

Here is a fun activity that will help you learn to spell your name and the names of your Frozen friends.

S v e n

You will need:
- ✳ a photo of yourself
- ✳ glue
- ✳ thin card
- ✳ scissors
- ✳ pen or pencil

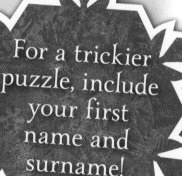

For a trickier puzzle, include your first name and surname!

What to do:

1. Print out a photo of yourself and stick it onto thin card.

2. Cut around the edge, leaving some writing space below.

3. Write your name, spacing the letters out equally along the width of the photo.

4. Cut the photo into vertical strips – one strip for each letter.

5. Mix up the strips and put your puzzle together again to spell your name.

Using these pictures, follow steps 1 to 5
from the opposite page.

Ask a grown-up to help
you when using scissors.

Place a snowflake sticker next to the things that you can do!

I can ...

※ say a word and hear the sound in it.

※ choose which letters make each sound.

I can ...

※ read and spell these tricky words (tick the boxes):

said		your		by	
says		be		my	
are		he		here	
were		me		there	
was		she		where	
is		we		love	
his		no		come	
has		friend		some	
you		so		one	
go					

I can ...

※ spell words with the suffixes -ing, -ed, -er, -est.

※ make plurals by adding -s or -es.

※ put two words together to make a new word.

※ change the meaning of a word by adding the prefix un-.

※ spell words with long vowel sounds.

※ spell words with more than one syllable.

More Activities to Share with Your Child

Some things to know about spelling in Year 1

Tricky words

There are 45 Common Exception Words – also known as 'tricky words' – listed in the National Curriculum for children to learn to spell in Year 1. These are tricky to spell because they have an unusual spelling of a sound in the word, such as the 'w' sound at the beginning of the word 'one'. Children are taught that these words have a tricky bit (because not all of the word is hard to spell). Children identify the tricky bit and then think of a way to remember the unusual spelling.

Use the ideas in this book to help your child create a way of remembering how to spell the tricky bit of these 45 words. Silly things and images really stick in our minds – so don't be afraid to come up with some funny ideas!

the	a	do	to	today	of	said	says	are
were	was	is	his	has	I	you	your	they
be	he	me	she	we	no	go	so	my
by	here	there	where	love	come	some	one	once
ask	friend	school	put	push	pull	full	house	our

Graphemes and phonemes

Your child learns to read and spell by understanding the phonic code. There are 44 sounds in the English language and each sound is called a **phoneme**. These are the sounds that we blend together to make words. 'C' 'a' 't' are the three sounds that make the word 'cat'.

A sound written down is called a **grapheme**. There are more than 150 ways to write down the 44 sounds in the English language. This is why it is so hard to spell accurately. The sound ai in the word rain can be written:

ay	play	eigh	sleigh
ai	rain	ey	they
a_e	make	aigh	straight
a	acorn		

In primary school, your child will learn to use all these graphemes so that they can spell accurately.

If your child needs help to spell a word, ask him or her to say the word out loud and then say the sounds in the word. Look back through the book for help to work out which graphemes to use. Often it is only one part of the word that is hard to work out. This way they will see that they can spell most of the word successfully – and only need to think hard about one tiny part.

Words can be expanded by adding prefixes to the beginning of them. When we add the prefix 'un' to a word, it changes its meaning to a negative: happy becomes unhappy.

Suffixes do the same thing to the end of words. These suffixes can be used to create verb tenses: -ing , -ed and -s, -es.

Word games to help spelling

Make up silly rhymes

First, start rhyming words out loud. Choose one word and take turns to think of other words that rhyme with it. Use the words to make up a silly poem. Then, write the words down. Do all the words that rhyme have the same letters at the end? Some words like **tea** and **me**, **row**, **go** and **toe** rhyme but have different ways of spelling the same sound. Challenge your child to find other words that rhyme but don't have the same spelling.

Make kennings

Centuries ago, the Vikings began using 'kennings' – where a compound of two words creates a new noun. For example, they might have called their sword *giant-slayer* or their ship *sea-rider*. A kenning describes something familiar in an uncommon way, without using its name. Lists of kennings were often used in Old Norse poetry.

Why not make your own kennings? You could think of new words to describe things that are important to you, or you could think of new ways to describe things you use every day. A parent could be a *hug-giver* or a spoon could be a *food-shoveller*!

Answers

Pages 6 to 7

a. Anna b. Elsa c. Bulda
d. Grand Pabbie e. Sven f. Little Rock
g. Sven h. Kristoff i. Olaf
j. Oaken
k. Arendelle
l. The Northern Lights

Page 8

ay	ai	a_e
day	paint	frame
stay	tail	shake
	wait	cage
	sail	late

Page 9

rain: ai play: ay cake: a_e

Page 10

a. Anna played outdoors on Monday.
b. Bulda gave Sven a treat on Tuesday.
c. Oaken worked hard on Wednesday.
d. Little Rock found two crystals on Thursday.
e. Elsa made magic on Friday.
f. Olaf and the Snowgies had fun on Saturday.
g. Kristoff went for a walk on Sunday.

Page 11

ee sound	igh sound
happy	cry
baby	dry
family	fly
funny	sty
party	try

Page 13

Page 14

a. well. b. buzz.
c. miss. d. off.
e. Elsa wears a beautiful blue dress.
f. Anna hiked up a snowy hill.
g. Olaf gives the flower a sniff.
h. Sven the reindeer has a coat of fuzz.

Page 15

a. Kristoff c. Anna
b. Arendelle d. Marshmallow

Page 16

a. outdoors d. friendship
b. moonlight e. waterfall
c. snowman

Page 17

be he there me
here she where we

Page 18

ow	oe	o_e	oa
snow	foe	stone	toast
blow	toe	alone	road
glow			boat
yellow			roast

Page 19

rock cod rod
not hop

hope note
code rode

Page 22

O|laf cry|stal snow|flake
moun|tain prin|cess ri|ver
wa|ter sis|ters

Page 23

a. reindeer e. yellow
b. snowball f. outside
c. antler g. Kristoff
d. birthday h. holiday

Page 24

a. hatch bench ditch patch church
b. beach watch stretch itch touch

Answers

Page 24 continued

ch	tch
bench	hatch
church	ditch
beach	patch
touch	watch
	stretch
	itch

Page 25

said	are	was	come
says	were	love	some

Page 26

walked	opened
lifted	rushed
licked	climbed
pulled	jumped

Page 27

carrying	kicking
singing	working
playing	sleeping
watching	holding

Page 28

sisters	boats
birds	horses
thrones	blocks

Page 29

dishes	boxes
branches	dresses
catches	buzzes

Page 31

Olaf – d	Sven – h

Page 32

a. Anna used to think her sister was unkind.
b. Olaf is never unhappy!
c. Skating on the ice is unsafe for reindeer.
d. Anna used a key to unlock the castle door.
e. Elsa was feeling unadventurous that day.
f. Marshmallow is an unfriendly snowman.

Page 33

is	his	has
you	your	no
go	so	by
my	I	

Page 34

oo	ue	ew	u_e
food	clue	grew	rule
soon	blue	few	rude
balloon	true	new	
	rescue		

Page 35

a. Little Rock whistled a happy tune.
b. Elsa was due home any minute.
c. Kristoff noticed it was a full moon.
d. The icy wind blew a chill through Arendelle.
e. Olaf always stays cool!
f. Marshmallow looks huge next to the Snowgies.

Page 36

a. Elsa needed a faster sled to reach the castle in time.
b. Anna wore a thicker cape to keep her warm.
c. The Northern Lights were brighter than Little Rock could ever have imagined.

Page 37

a. Anna is bigger than Olaf, but Marshmallow is the biggest.
b. Elsa was quicker to climb the tree than Kristoff, but Anna was quickest.
c. Monday was colder than Tuesday, but Friday was the coldest.

From the Movie

Disney

FROZEN
MAGIC OF THE NORTHERN LIGHTS

CONGRATULATIONS!

_____
(Name)

has completed the Disney Learning Workbook:

Spelling Practice

Presented on

_____
(Date)

_____
(Parent's Signature)

From the Movie

Disney
FROZEN
MAGIC OF THE
NORTHERN LIGHTS